GIFTED & TALENTED®

*To develop
your child's gifts
and talents*

ATLAS

A Reference Workbook for Ages 6-8

Written by Mary Hill and Martha Cheney
Illustrated by Larry Nolte

Lowell House
Juvenile
Los Angeles

CONTEMPORARY BOOKS
Chicago

Manufactured in the United States of America

ISBN: 1 56565-238-X

10 9 8 7 6 5 4 3 2 1

Lowell House books can be purchased at special discounts when ordered in bulk for premiums and special sales.
Contact Department VH at the following address:
Lowell House Juvenile
2029 Century Park East
Suite 3290
Los Angeles, CA 90067

GIFTED & TALENTED® REFERENCE WORKBOOKS will help develop your child's natural talents and gifts by providing questions and pencil activities to enhance critical and creative thinking skills. These skills of logic and reasoning teach children **how** to think. They are precisely the skills emphasized by teachers of gifted and talented children.

Thinking skills are the skills needed to be able to learn anything at any time. If a child has a grasp of how to think, school success and even success in life will become more assured. In addition, the child will become self-confident as he or she approaches new tasks with the ability to think them through and discover solutions.

GIFTED & TALENTED® REFERENCE WORKBOOKS present these skills in a unique way, combining the basic subject areas of reading, language arts, and math with dictionary skills, map skills, and other reference-book skills. Here are some of the thinking skills you will find:

- Deduction — the ability to reach a logical conclusion by interpreting clues

- Understanding Relationships — the ability to recognize how objects, shapes, and words are similar or dissimilar; to classify and categorize

- Sequencing — the ability to organize events, numbers; to recognize patterns

- Inference — the ability to reach logical conclusions from given or assumed evidence

- Creative Thinking — the ability to generate unique ideas; to compare and contrast the same elements in different situations; to present imaginative solutions to problems

Each book contains thinking activities that challenge children. You may need to work with your child on many of the pages, especially with the child who is a nonreader. However, even a nonreader can master thinking skills, and the sooner your child learns how to think, the better. Read the books with your child and, if necessary, explain the activities. Let your child choose to answer the questions or do the activities that interest him or her. When interest wanes, stop. A page or two at a time may be enough, as the child should have fun while learning.

It is important to remember that these activities are designed to teach your child **how to think,** not how to find the right answer. Teachers of gifted children are never surprised when a child discovers a new "right" answer. For example, a child may be asked to choose the object that doesn't belong in this group: a table, a chair, a book, a desk. The best answer is **book,** since all the others are furniture. But a child could respond that all of them belong because they all could be found in an office or a library. The best way to react to this type of response is to praise the child and gently point out that there is another answer, too. While creativity should be encouraged, your child must look for the best and most **suitable** answer.

GIFTED AND TALENTED® REFERENCE WORKBOOKS have been written by teachers. Educationally sound and endorsed by a leader in the gifted field, this series will benefit any child who demonstrates curiosity, imagination, a sense of fun and wonder about the world, and a desire to learn. These books will open your child's mind to new experiences and help fulfill his or her true potential.

THE EARTH

This is a picture of Earth.
You would see this on your way to the moon.

This is a map of Earth.
Somewhere on Earth there is a little girl named Ann.
Where on Earth is she?

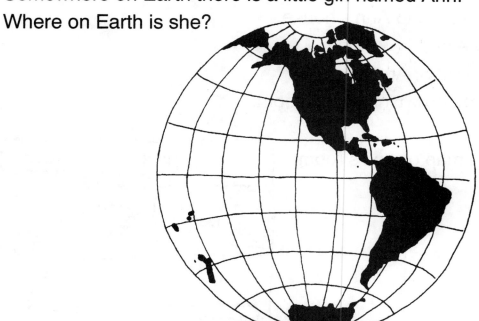

ANN'S HOUSE

This is Ann's house.

One day a giant came to Ann's house.

He wanted to see her.

He lifted off the roof of Ann's house.

He looked straight down into Ann's room.

This is a map of Ann's room:

What does your room look like? In the box below, draw a map of your room. Be sure to label everything! The words in the Word Bank at the bottom of the page may be helpful.

Word Bank

bed	toy box	desk
bookshelf	chest of drawers	closet
dresser	bedside table	window
rug	lamp	poster

ANN'S STREET

Ann's house is next to Billy's house and Jane's house. The children are all friends. They live on the same street.

The giant put the roof back on Ann's house. He looked straight down at Ann's street.

This is what he saw:

This is a map of Ann's street.

Does your street look like this?

ANN'S ADDRESS

"Where do you live?" the giant roared at Ann.

"Please do not shout!" Ann said. "I live here."

"Where is that?" the giant whispered. "Do you know your address?"

"Yes," Ann said. "It is 123 Main Street."

"How do you know?" the giant asked.

"I will show you," Ann answered.

Ann pointed to her front door. "123," it read.

"It does not say Main Street," the giant growled. "How do you know you live on Main Street?"

Ann walked to the corner. She pointed to a sign. It said, "Main Street."

"That is how I know," Ann said.

Write a letter to Ann and tell her where you live. Label the envelope correctly. Turn to page 16 to find out the rest of Ann's address. Be sure to write your return address in the upper left corner of the envelope. Draw a stamp in the upper right corner. Find out how much a stamp costs and write that number on the stamp.

Dear Ann,

your name

your street

your city and state   your zip code

Ann's address: _____

Why is your address important? Why do you need to know your address? If you ever need help from the police or fire department, they can find you if you tell them your address! Every day, except Sundays and holidays, your mail carrier brings your family its mail. The mail carrier knows which home to deliver it to because you have an address!

Follow the maze, beginning at START, to help the mail carrier deliver your letter to Ann's house. You know her address!

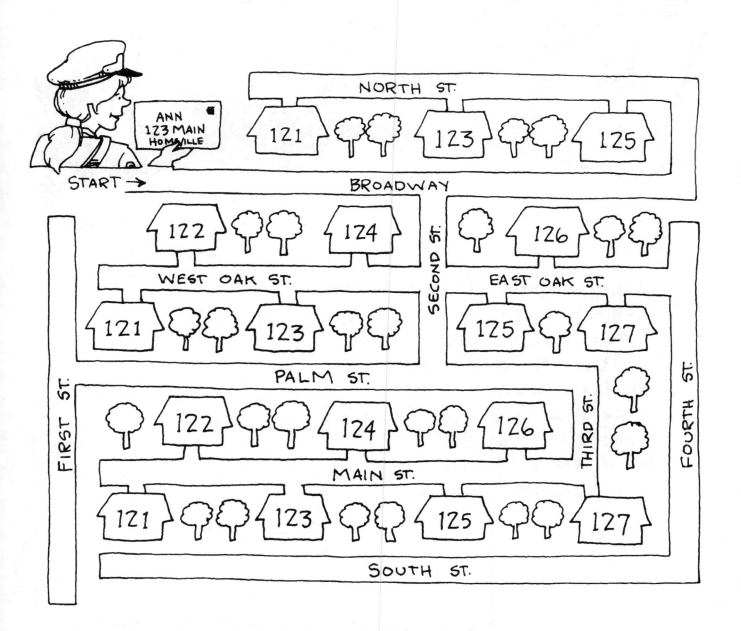

The giant pointed to the street with his great big finger.

"Then this is Main Street," he said, "and that is Cross Street. And that is your house. It says '123.'"

"Right!" Ann said. "And that is Billy's house. It says '121.' And that is Jane's house. It says '125.'"

What would the giant see if he came to visit your street? Draw a map of your street as it would look from the giant's point of view. Be sure to label everything! The words in the Word Bank may be helpful.

Word Bank

street	road	avenue
house	apartment	sidewalk
store	building	fence
wall	sign	tree
hill	traffic light	driveway

ANN'S TOWN

The giant took a step away.
This is what he saw:

Then he stood up very tall and looked at his feet.
This is what he saw:

"Everything looks like a map," the giant said.
"But there are no names. What town is this?"
he asked.

"It is Homeville," Ann said.

"How do you know?" the giant asked.

"There is a sign on the road that says so,"
Ann said.

And there it was:

What town or city do you live in? Is it anything like Ann's town? Is there a sign with your town's name on it? What does it say?

In the space below, draw a map of your town. Don't forget to label it! The Word Banks on this page and on page 13 might be helpful.

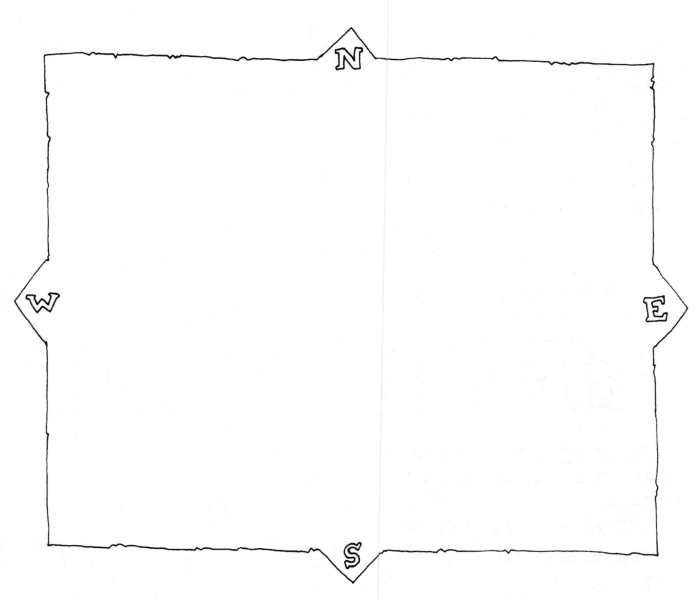

Word Bank

fire station	police station	bus stop
restaurant	park	school
doctor's office	market	library
movie theater	bowling alley	airport

ANN'S STATE

"So what is your address?" the giant asked.

Ann said, "Ann Miller
123 Main Street
Homeville, California, 92109.

"Why do you want to know?" she asked the giant.

The giant hung his head. "I am lost," he said. "I have looked for my home, but I cannot find it."

"Is it in California?" Ann asked. "That's the state I live in."

"What's a state?" the Giant asked. "If I stand up tall, will I see one?"

"Sure!" Ann said.

Here is what the giant saw:

THE UNITED STATES

"But where is California?" the giant asked.

"My father has a book with maps in it," Ann said. "I will get it."

Ann opened the book. "ATLAS," the title read.

"There is the United States," the giant said.

"What do the pictures mean?" Ann asked.

This is what Ann and the giant saw:

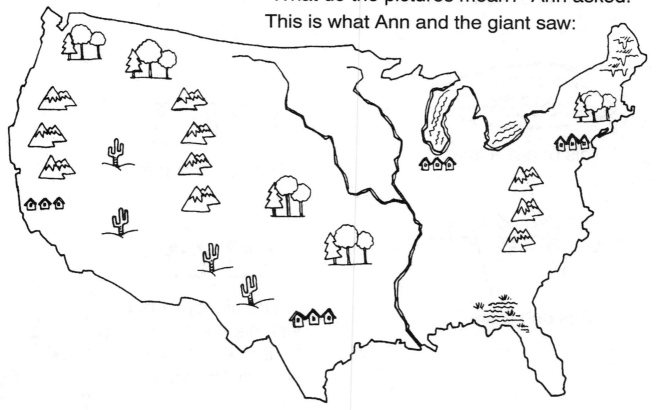

Can you guess what any of the pictures mean?

Ann turned the page. "I see," she said. "This guide explains what the pictures mean.

"This one is mountains.

This one is a desert.

This one is a swamp.

This one is a river.

This one is a lake.

This one is a forest.

This one is ice."

The giant pointed with his great big finger. "And this one is a city," he said.

The pictures that explain what we see on a map are called symbols. Draw a line from each symbol below to the name of the place each shows us on a map.

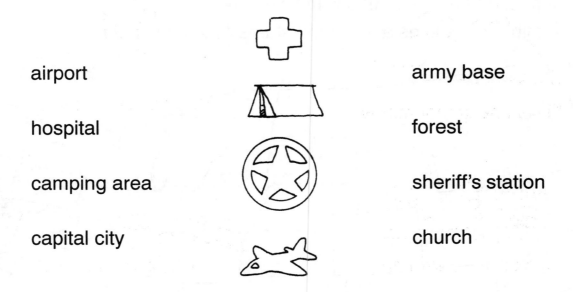

airport

hospital

camping area

capital city

army base

forest

sheriff's station

church

Can you make up some symbols of your own? Pretend you are a map maker. In the space below, draw the symbols you would use to show the places listed at the bottom of the page.

ocean   park   fire station

THE UNITED STATES

Ann said, "Here is a map with lines."
"Maybe those lines are around states," the giant said.

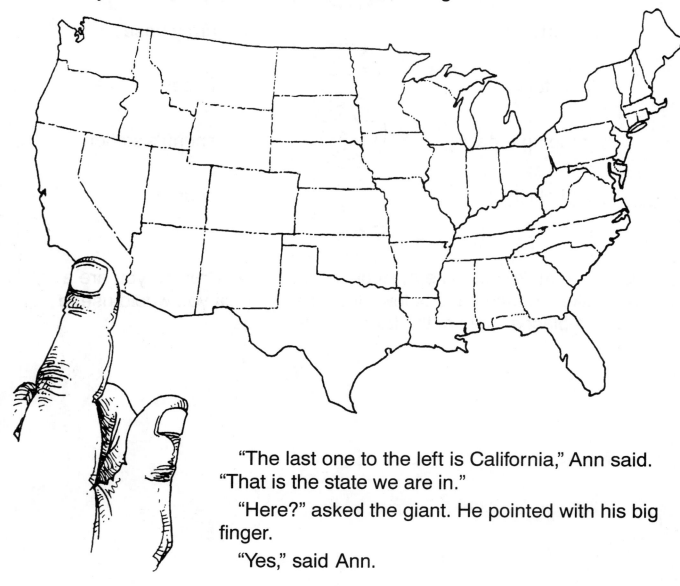

"The last one to the left is California," Ann said.
"That is the state we are in."

"Here?" asked the giant. He pointed with his big finger.

"Yes," said Ann.

If you live in the United States, try to find the state you live in.
Were you born there? If not, point to the state where you were born.
Do you know the names of any other states?

Look at the maps on pages 22, 26, and 27. Study the names of the states, their shapes, and their locations. When you think you can remember some of them, turn back to this page. Try to identify each state using this blank map.

STATES, COUNTRIES, AND CONTINENTS

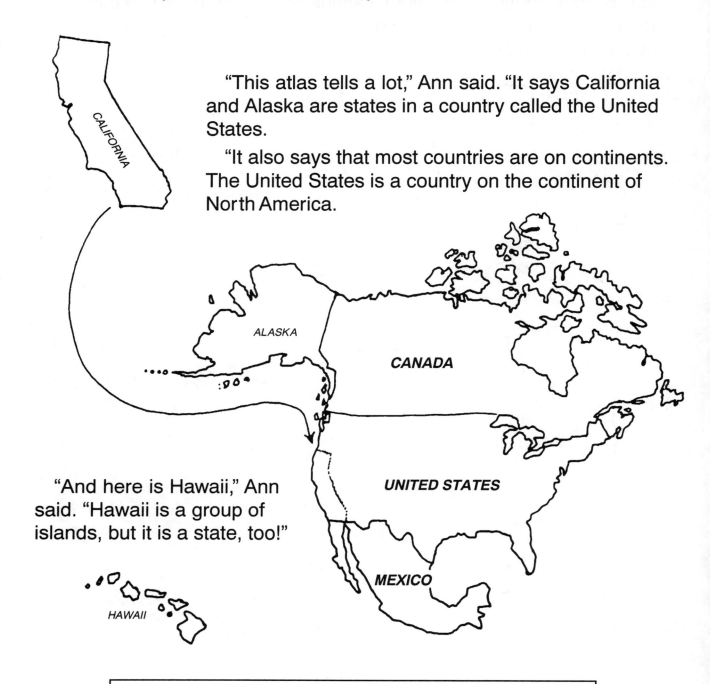

"This atlas tells a lot," Ann said. "It says California and Alaska are states in a country called the United States.

"It also says that most countries are on continents. The United States is a country on the continent of North America.

"And here is Hawaii," Ann said. "Hawaii is a group of islands, but it is a state, too!"

A continent is a very large piece of land. There are seven continents on the Earth.

After you have read this book, you will be able to name all seven of them!

HAWAII AND ALASKA

"Do you live in Hawaii?" Ann asked the giant.

"No. Hawaii is warm. It is always cold where I live."

KAUAI

OAHU

MAUI

HAWAII

HAWAII

ATLAS

Ann pointed to the map. "Look at all the ice in Alaska! It must be cold there," she said.

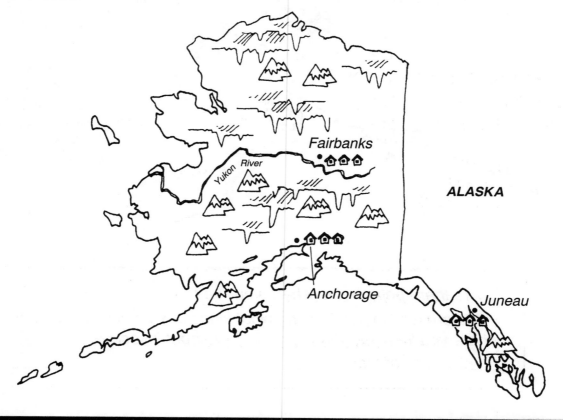

Fairbanks

Yukon River

ALASKA

Anchorage

Juneau

"Do you live in Alaska?" Ann asked the giant.

"No, there are no polar bears or forget-me-nots where I live," he said.

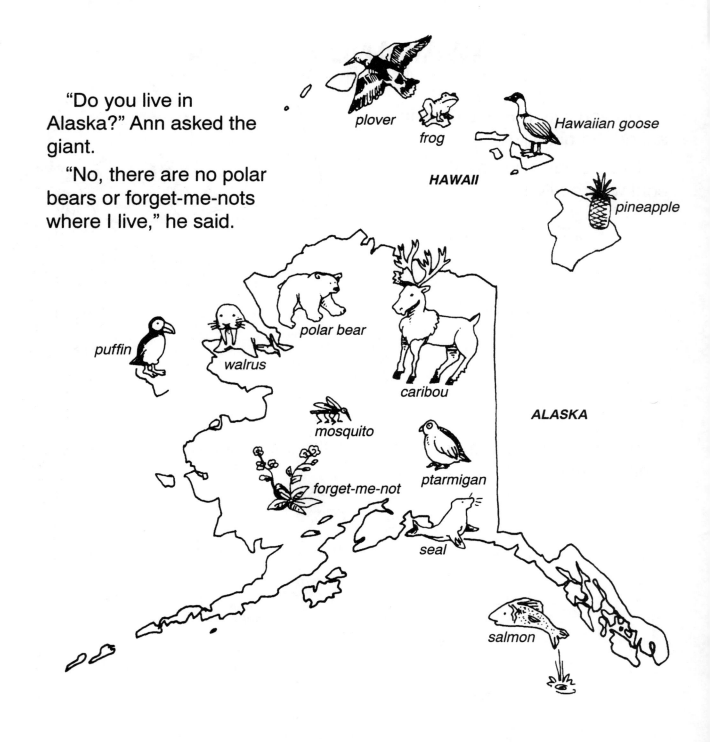

Are there polar bears where you live?

If there are no polar bears, what kinds of animals can you see where you live? Are there birds? How about insects?

In the space below, draw some pictures of the animals that live near you. These should be animals that roam free, not pets or zoo animals. Be sure to label your drawings!

THE WESTERN UNITED STATES

Ann turned the page of her father's book.

"There is an ocean to the left," Ann said.

"That way is west," the giant said. "I can tell by the picture above the map. It has arrows that show which way is north, south, east, or west."

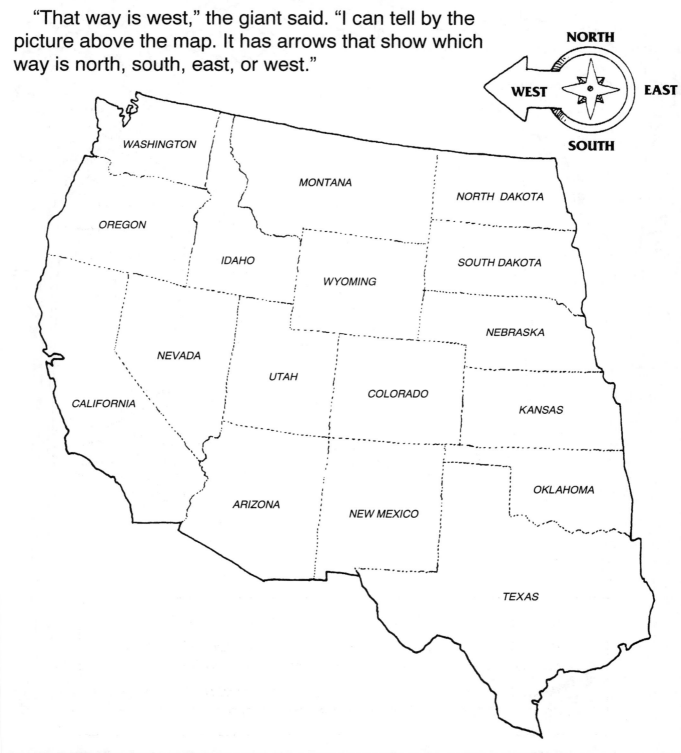

THE EASTERN UNITED STATES

"There is another ocean to the right," Ann said.

"That way is east," the giant said. "Look at all the states!"

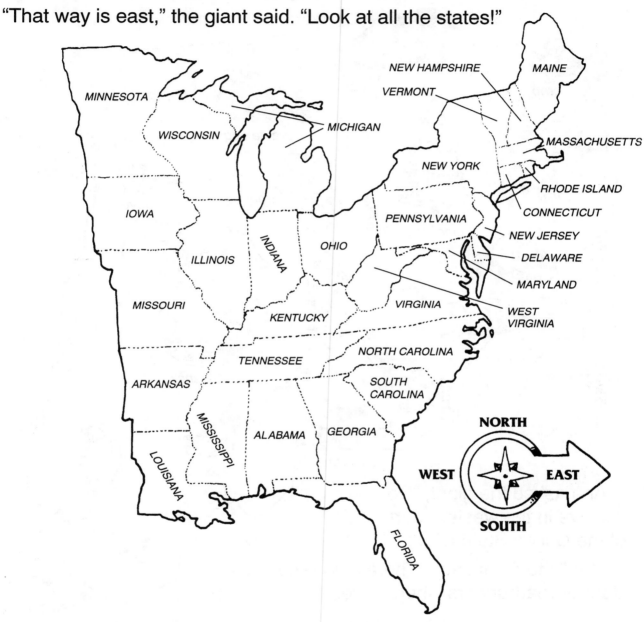

Do you know the difference between east and west?

Ask someone to point out east to you. You can remember it because the sun comes up in the east in the morning.

Ask someone to point out west to you. You can remember it because the sun goes down in the west at night.

THE WESTERN UNITED STATES

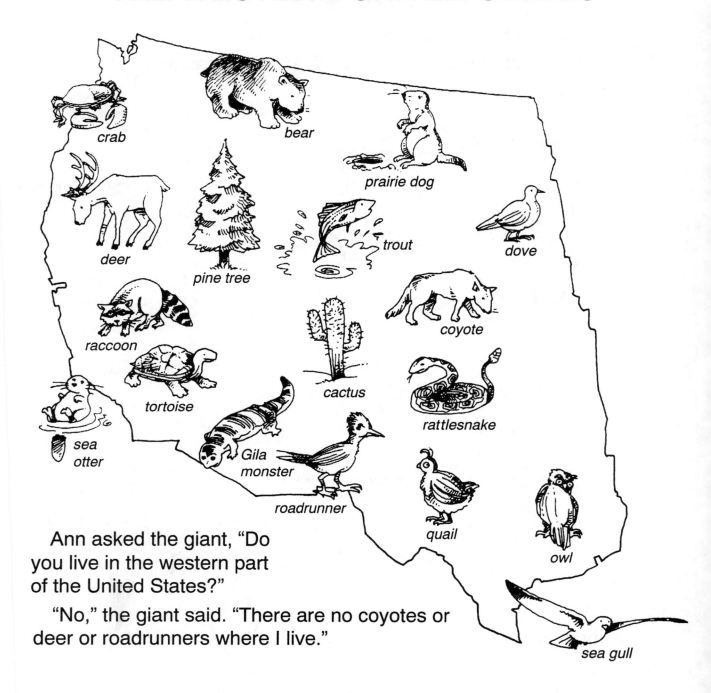

crab

bear

prairie dog

deer

pine tree

trout

dove

raccoon

cactus

coyote

tortoise

rattlesnake

sea otter

Gila monster

roadrunner

quail

owl

sea gull

Ann asked the giant, "Do you live in the western part of the United States?"

"No," the giant said. "There are no coyotes or deer or roadrunners where I live."

Have you ever seen a coyote? What other animals do coyotes look like? Coyotes howl when they are going home. Why do you think they do that?

THE EASTERN UNITED STATES

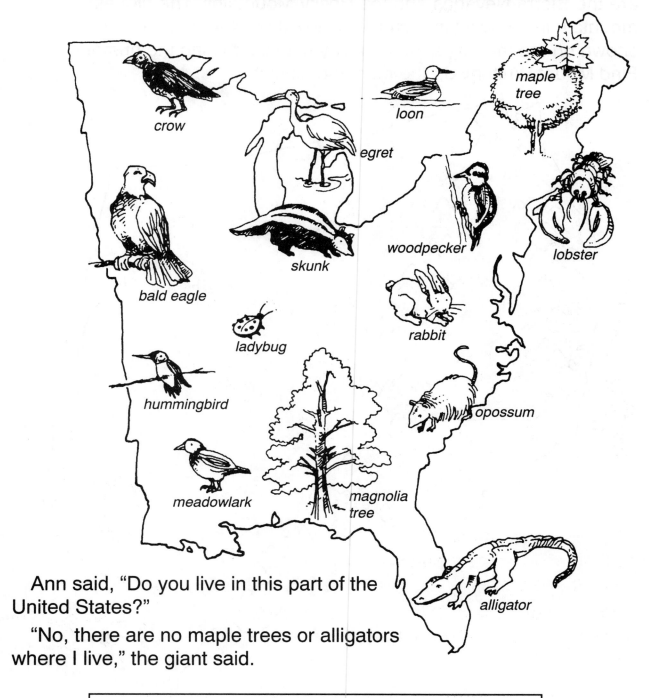

crow

loon

maple tree

egret

woodpecker

lobster

bald eagle

skunk

rabbit

ladybug

hummingbird

opossum

meadowlark

magnolia tree

alligator

Ann said, "Do you live in this part of the United States?"

"No, there are no maple trees or alligators where I live," the giant said.

Can you find the maple leaf on the map?

Maybe there is a maple tree in your neighborhood.

How many kinds of trees can you see in your neighborhood?

The large mountain ranges in the western part of the United States are the Sierra Nevadas and the Rocky Mountains. The highest mountain in the west is Mount Whitney. It is 14,494 feet high! It is shown on the map by a mountain symbol containing the number 1. Find Mount Whitney on the map and label it.

Look at both sides of the map. Color the areas with mountain symbols brown. Look for the Great Lakes and color them blue.

The large mountain range in the eastern part of the United States is the Appalachian Mountains. The highest mountain in the east is Mount Mitchell. It is only 6,684 feet high. It is shown on the map by a mountain symbol containing the number 2. Find Mount Mitchell on the map and label it.

Look at both sides of the map. Find the area marked Coastal Plain and color it green. Look for the areas marked Great Plains and color them yellow.

NORTH AMERICA

Ann turned the page.

"Here is all of North America," she said.

The giant nodded. "There is the United States, and Canada, and Mexico," he said.

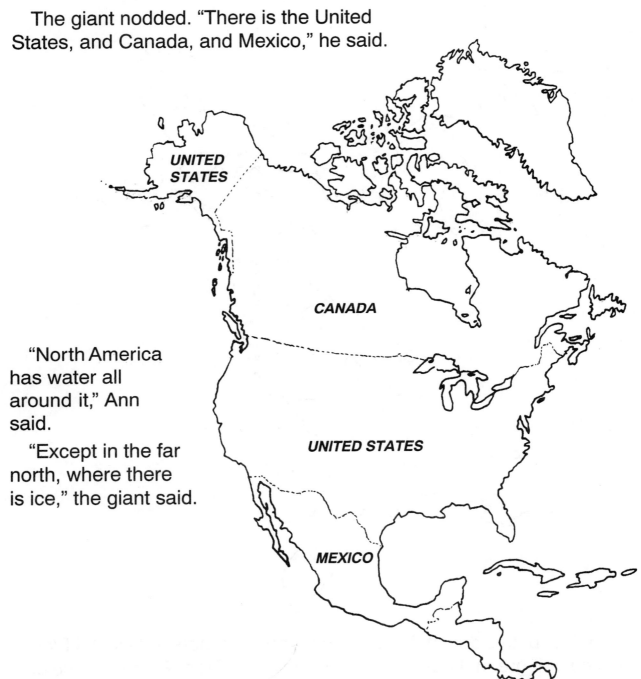

"North America has water all around it," Ann said.

"Except in the far north, where there is ice," the giant said.

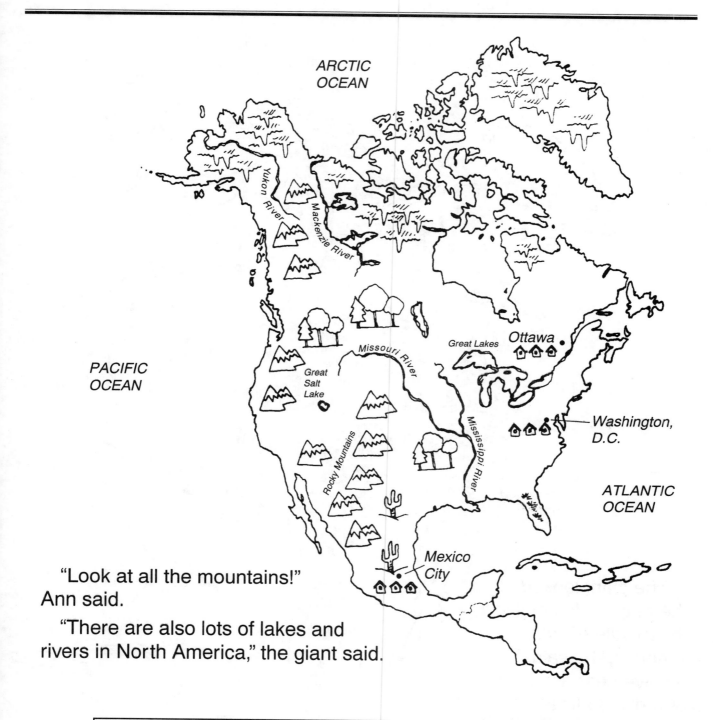

ARCTIC OCEAN

PACIFIC OCEAN

Yukon River

Mackenzie River

Missouri River

Great Salt Lake

Rocky Mountains

Great Lakes

Ottawa

Mississippi River

Washington, D.C.

ATLANTIC OCEAN

Mexico City

"Look at all the mountains!" Ann said.

"There are also lots of lakes and rivers in North America," the giant said.

Have you ever traveled to the mountains?

Name some things you might see there.

Do you think it would be colder in the mountains?

Pretend you are going on a trip. What are some of the things you would take with you to the mountains?

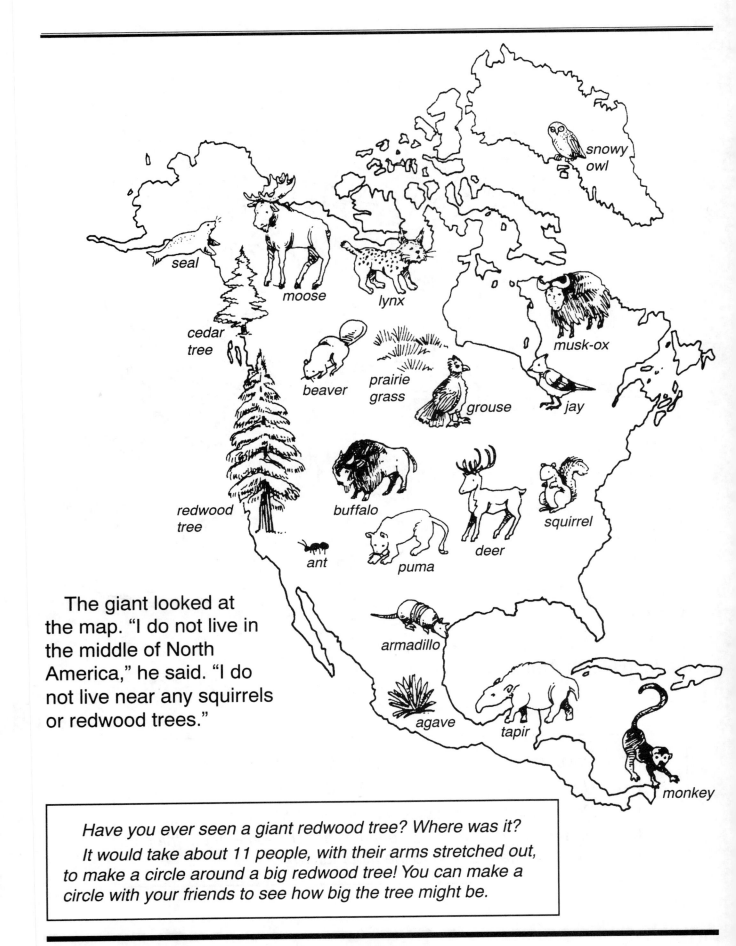

snowy owl

seal

moose

lynx

musk-ox

cedar tree

beaver

prairie grass

grouse

jay

redwood tree

buffalo

deer

squirrel

ant

puma

The giant looked at the map. "I do not live in the middle of North America," he said. "I do not live near any squirrels or redwood trees."

armadillo

agave

tapir

monkey

Have you ever seen a giant redwood tree? Where was it?

It would take about 11 people, with their arms stretched out, to make a circle around a big redwood tree! You can make a circle with your friends to see how big the tree might be.

Mexico is the United States' next-door neighbor to the south. In Mexico you can climb thousands of steps that lead to a temple built by the Aztec people hundreds of years ago! You can shop in an open-air market and eat delicious, freshly made tortillas.

Create a little bit of Mexico in your own kitchen with this delicious idea. Make your own tortillas, which are flat, round pieces of bread. Ask an adult to help you.

A Treat From Mexico

2 cups flour

1/2 teaspoon salt

1/4 cup solid shortening or lard

1/2 cup water

1. Mix flour and salt together in a bowl. Add shortening by rubbing it into the flour with your fingers. Now stir in the water to make a soft dough.

2. Shape the dough into 12 balls and set them aside for 15 minutes. Pat each ball into a flat pancake and then roll it out with a rolling pin until it is about 8 inches across.

3. Cook the tortillas on a griddle or in a skillet until they start to bubble and turn slightly brown.

4. You can eat the tortillas on their own, or use them to make sandwiches. Fill them with rice and beans, cheese, vegetables, or anything you like!

CANADA

"Canada is very big," Ann said.

"It does not have many states," said the giant.

"In Canada they are not called states," said Ann. "My mother said they are called provinces and territories."

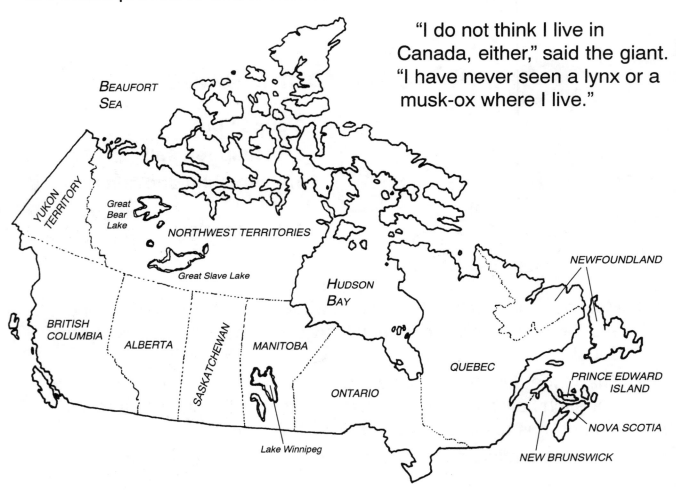

"I do not think I live in Canada, either," said the giant. "I have never seen a lynx or a musk-ox where I live."

BEAUFORT SEA

YUKON TERRITORY

Great Bear Lake

NORTHWEST TERRITORIES

Great Slave Lake

HUDSON BAY

NEWFOUNDLAND

BRITISH COLUMBIA

ALBERTA

SASKATCHEWAN

MANITOBA

ONTARIO

QUEBEC

PRINCE EDWARD ISLAND

NOVA SCOTIA

Lake Winnipeg

NEW BRUNSWICK

Some people who live in the northern part of Canada make their houses out of snow in winter. Have you ever made an igloo? How would you do it?

The musk-ox of Canada is a cousin of the buffalo. Can you find each of these animals on the map on page 34?

A musk-ox is big and furry. Do you think it looks like a buffalo? How are a musk-ox and a buffalo different?

MEXICO

"Here is a map of Mexico," Ann said. "Do you live there?"

"No, I do not live in Mexico," the giant said. "There are no vultures or anteaters or armadillos where I live."

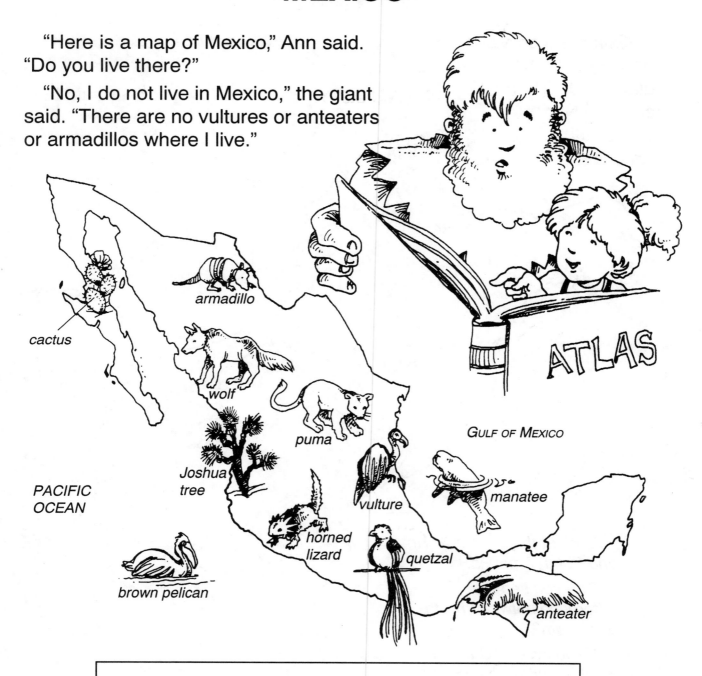

ATLAS

cactus

armadillo

wolf

puma

Joshua tree

PACIFIC OCEAN

GULF OF MEXICO

vulture

horned lizard

manatee

quetzal

brown pelican

anteater

If you lived in Mexico, in what direction would you walk to get to Canada?

Would you walk through the United States? What is that direction called?

You can check your answer on page 32.

NORTH AND SOUTH AMERICA

"Sometimes I stand up very tall," the giant said. "Then I can see North *and* South America."

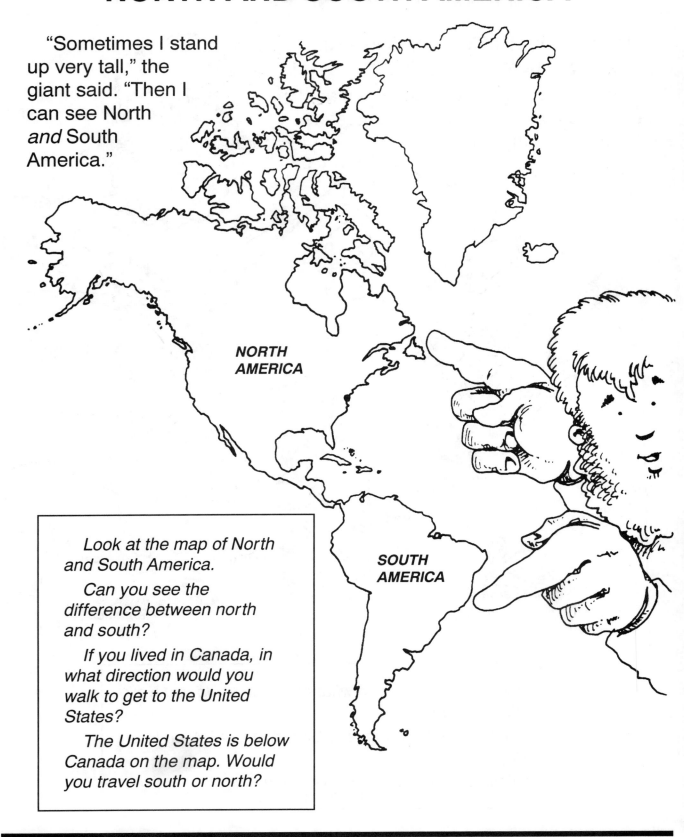

NORTH AMERICA

SOUTH AMERICA

Look at the map of North and South America.

Can you see the difference between north and south?

If you lived in Canada, in what direction would you walk to get to the United States?

The United States is below Canada on the map. Would you travel south or north?

A compass is an instrument used to tell direction. Maps have a special symbol called a compass rose. It has points that stick out, much like the petals on a flower. This is why it is known as a compass rose.

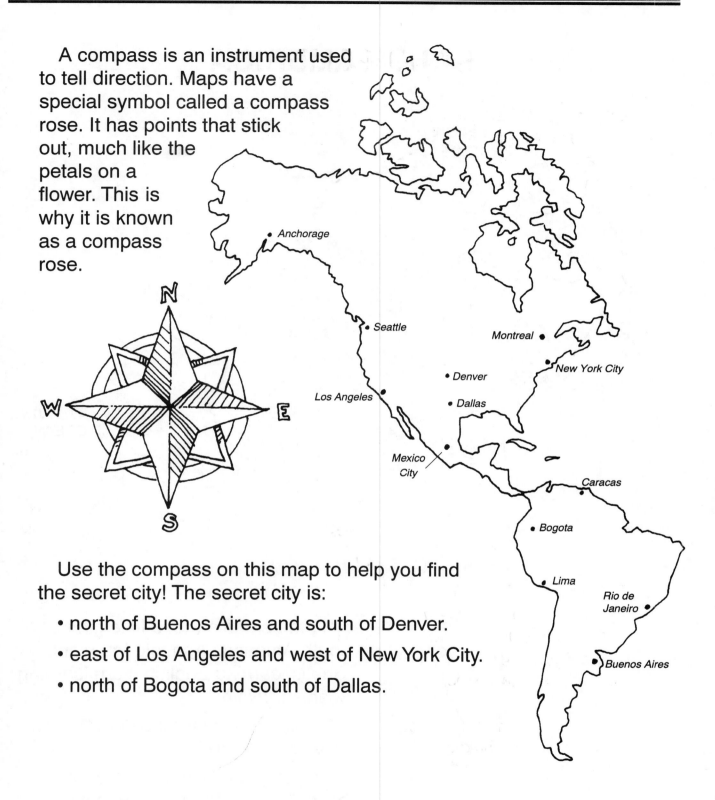

Use the compass on this map to help you find the secret city! The secret city is:

- north of Buenos Aires and south of Denver.
- east of Los Angeles and west of New York City.
- north of Bogota and south of Dallas.

SOUTH AMERICA

"I am pen pals with a little girl in South America," Ann told the giant. "She is learning English. I am learning Spanish. *¡Hola!*"

"*¡Hola!*" the giant repeated. "What does that mean?"

"*¡Hola!* is the Spanish word for 'hello,'" Ann said. "Most people in Mexico and South America speak Spanish!"

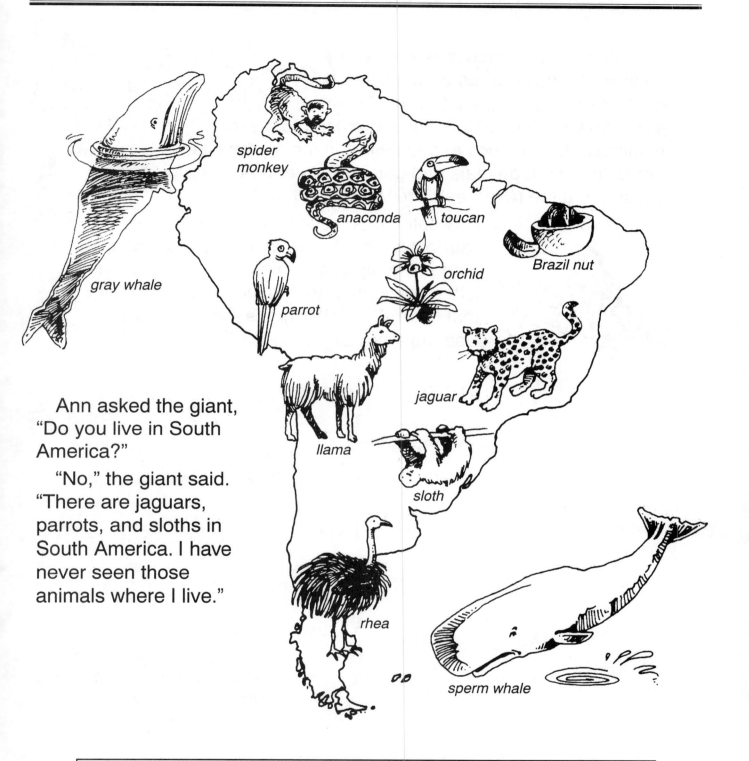

spider monkey

anaconda

toucan

Brazil nut

orchid

gray whale

parrot

jaguar

llama

sloth

Ann asked the giant, "Do you live in South America?"

"No," the giant said. "There are jaguars, parrots, and sloths in South America. I have never seen those animals where I live."

rhea

sperm whale

Look for the jaguar on the map.
What animal family do you think the jaguar belongs to?
Jaguars have spots like leopards. Can you find a leopard in this book?
Jaguars are the only big members of their family that do not roar.

Much of South America is covered by rainforests. These areas of heavy rainfall are home to many special kinds of plants and animals. Some of the plants are used to make medicines. Many tribes of people live in the rainforests. There, they hunt animals and gather fruits and nuts for food. You can see that the rainforests are very important!

Create an acrostic poem using the word **rainforest** as a frame. Write a word that tells something about the rainforest across each letter. Remember that the word must contain that letter. One letter has been done for you. Use the Word Bank for help if you need it.

r
a
i
n
rainfall
o
r
e
s
t

Word Bank	tropical	animals	plants
	trees	medicines	tribes
	nuts	fruits	South America

The Amazon River is the largest river in the world. It runs all the way across the top of South America. It starts in the country of Peru and ends in the country of Brazil. There, it empties into the Atlantic Ocean. In the waters of the Amazon, you can find snakes, alligators, and piranha. Piranha are small fish that attack in groups and can eat large animals in only a few minutes!

Trace your finger over the path of the Amazon on page 40. Then try to complete this crossword puzzle.

Across

2. The Amazon River is found in South _____ .

5. large reptiles

6. small fish that attack in groups

7. country where the Amazon ends

Down

3. The Amazon empties into the _____ Ocean .

4. The Amazon is the _____ river in the world.

6. country where the Amazon begins

EUROPE

Ann turned the page. "This is a map of Europe," she told the giant. "Maybe you live there! My grandparents lived in Europe. It is a continent."

Europe is not as big as North America or South America, but it has a lot of countries.

Have you ever been to Europe?

People in Europe speak many different languages.

People in Spain speak Spanish. People in Italy speak Italian.

What language do people in France speak?

What language do people who live in England speak?

Do you know words in any other languages?

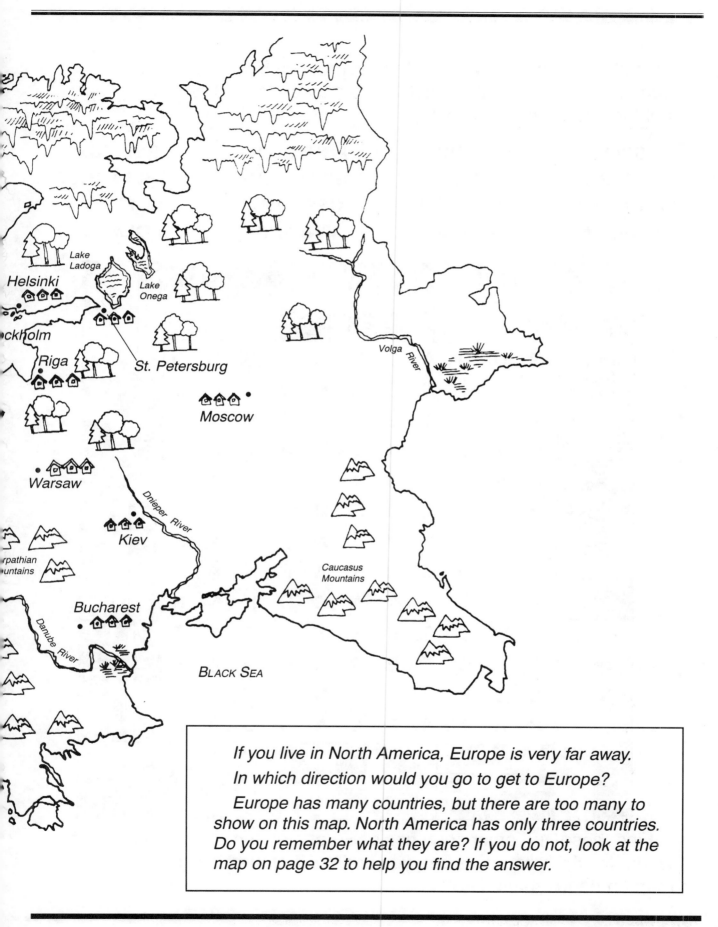

Lake
Ladoga

Helsinki

Lake
Onega

ckholm

Riga

St. Petersburg

Volga River

Moscow

Warsaw

Dnieper River

Kiev

rpathian
untains

Caucasus
Mountains

Bucharest

Danube River

BLACK SEA

If you live in North America, Europe is very far away.
In which direction would you go to get to Europe?
Europe has many countries, but there are too many to
show on this map. North America has only three countries.
Do you remember what they are? If you do not, look at the
map on page 32 to help you find the answer.

Find the names of some of the countries of Europe in the word search below. Remember that words may be found from left to right, right to left, or up and down.

SPAIN	FRANCE	PORTUGAL	IRELAND
GREECE	ITALY	SWITZERLAND	NETHERLANDS
ENGLAND	SCOTLAND	GERMANY	NORWAY
SWEDEN	DENMARK	FINLAND	POLAND

B D N A L T O C S C D
E F I N L A N D P G S
S W I T Z E R L A N D
H I T J K L M A I G N
O P A D N A L G N E A
P O L A N D Q U R R L
S T Y U V L X T Y M R
Z Y D E N M A R K A E
V I R Y A W R O N N H
S W E D E N T P S Y T
P E C E E R G M N K E
L J E F R A N C E D N
C B I R E L A N D A D

Find these and other countries of Europe on a map or a globe of the world. In which countries can you find each of the cities shown on the map on pages 44 and 45?

There are many wonderful things to see in Europe. In Paris, France, you can see the Eiffel Tower. It was built a long time ago, in the year 1889. The Eiffel Tower is 984 feet tall. It is made of iron and steel bars that are very strong, but they look like delicate lace.

Complete the missing half of the Eiffel Tower. (**Hint:** The tower is symmetrical. This means that it is exactly the same on both sides.)

Visit the library to find out more about Paris and the Eiffel Tower.

"Is your home in Europe?" Ann asked the giant.

He shook his head. "I've never seen a wild boar or a bat or a stork where I live," he said.

Have you ever seen a cuckoo clock? Do you think there was a real cuckoo in it? Look for the cuckoo on the map.

Europe has wild pigs called wild boars. How are they different from the pigs you have seen?

Europe also has reindeer that people can milk. Milk comes from other animals, too. Can you name them?

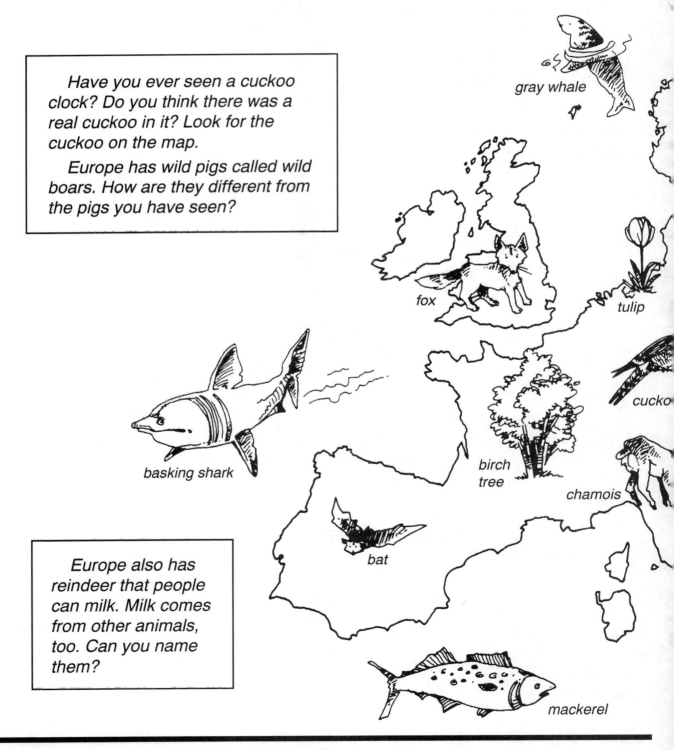

gray whale

fox

tulip

cucko

basking shark

birch tree

chamois

bat

mackerel

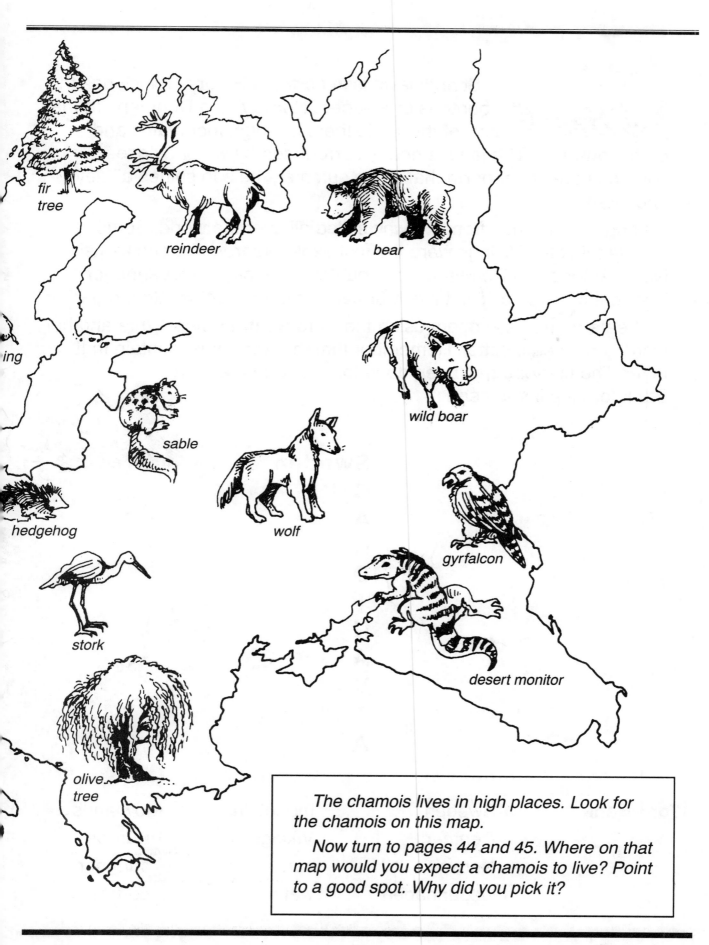

fir tree

reindeer

bear

ing

wild boar

sable

hedgehog

wolf

gyrfalcon

stork

desert monitor

olive tree

The chamois lives in high places. Look for the chamois on this map.

Now turn to pages 44 and 45. Where on that map would you expect a chamois to live? Point to a good spot. Why did you pick it?

Scandinavia is in northern Europe. It includes the countries of Sweden, Norway, and Denmark. In that part of the world there are high mountains and pretty lowlands. The land is nearly surrounded by water. These countries are so far north that in the summer, the sun shines all day and night!

Long ago, Vikings from Norway sailed all over the world. Some people think the Vikings were the first explorers from Europe to visit North America. In Denmark, you could visit the city of Copenhagen. There, the statue of The Little Mermaid welcomes ships into the harbor.

Create an acrostic poem using the word **Scandinavia**. Write another word across each letter. Remember that the word must contain that letter. The first one has been done for you. Use the Word Bank for help if you need it.

Sweden
C
A
N
D
I
N
A
V
I
A

Word Bank

Sweden	mountains	lowlands
Denmark	Vikings	Europe
Norway	sun	summer
Copenhagen	water	coastline

Unscramble the names of these animals that live in Europe. Then point to the picture that matches each name. Use the map on pages 48 and 49 if you need help.

REAB   _ _ _ _
LASBE   _ _ _ _ _
GOGHEHED   _ _ _ _ _ _ _ _
OXF   _ _ _
MOCHIAS   _ _ _ _ _ _ _
TAB   _ _ _
DRNEIREE   _ _ _ _ _ _ _ _
INLEGMM   _ _ _ _ _ _ _
OCKOUC   _ _ _ _ _ _
DWLI RABO   _ _ _ _ _ _ _ _
FLAGYONCR   _ _ _ _ _ _ _ _ _
KROST   _ _ _ _ _
FLOW   _ _ _ _
SEDTER   _ _ _ _ _ _
OMNTIOR   _ _ _ _ _ _ _

Use an encyclopedia to find out more about these animals.

ASIA

"Here is a map of Asia," Ann said.

"Asia is a very big continent!" the giant said.

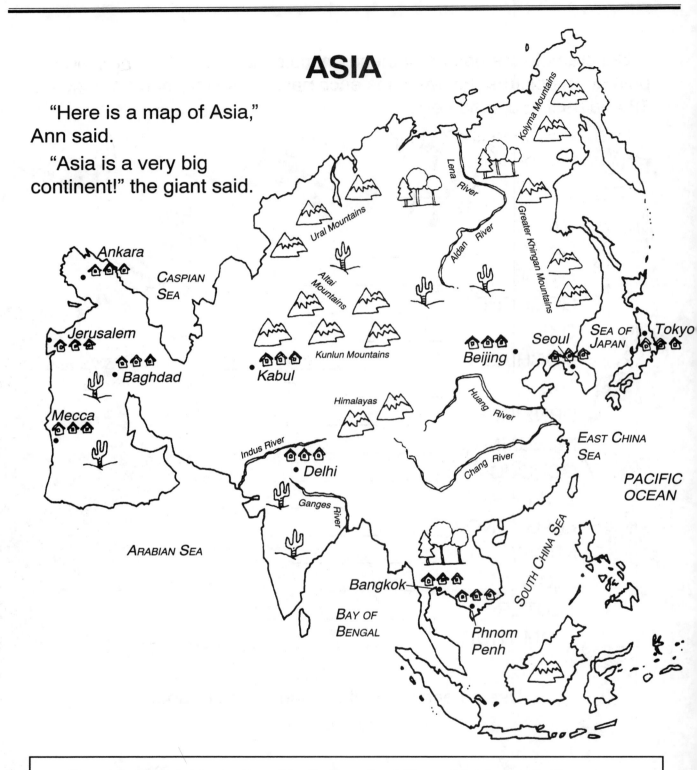

Does Asia look bigger than North America? Does it look smaller?

If you cannot tell, turn to pages 68 and 69. Which continent is larger?

You can tell how far away places are by how far apart they are on a map. Look at this map of Asia. Do you think it is farther from the city of Jerusalem to Baghdad, or from Beijing to Tokyo?

The huge wall pictured below was built over 2,000 years ago. It was built to keep out people who might try to attack the country of China. The wall stretches for more than 1,500 miles through the country.

Use the code to find out the name of this amazing structure. Fill in your answer below.

26	25	24	23	22	21	20	19	18	17	16	15	14
A	B	C	D	E	F	G	H	I	J	K	L	M

13	12	11	10	9	8	7	6	5	4	3	2	1
N	O	P	Q	R	S	T	U	V	W	X	Y	Z

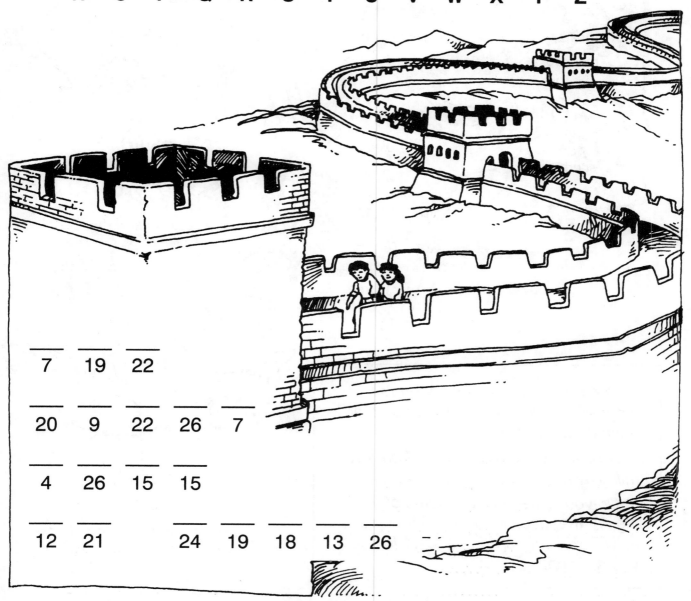

7   19   22

20   9   22   26   7

4   26   15   15

12   21   24   19   18   13   26

"But I know I do not live in Asia," the giant said. "There are no tigers or camels or poppies where I live."

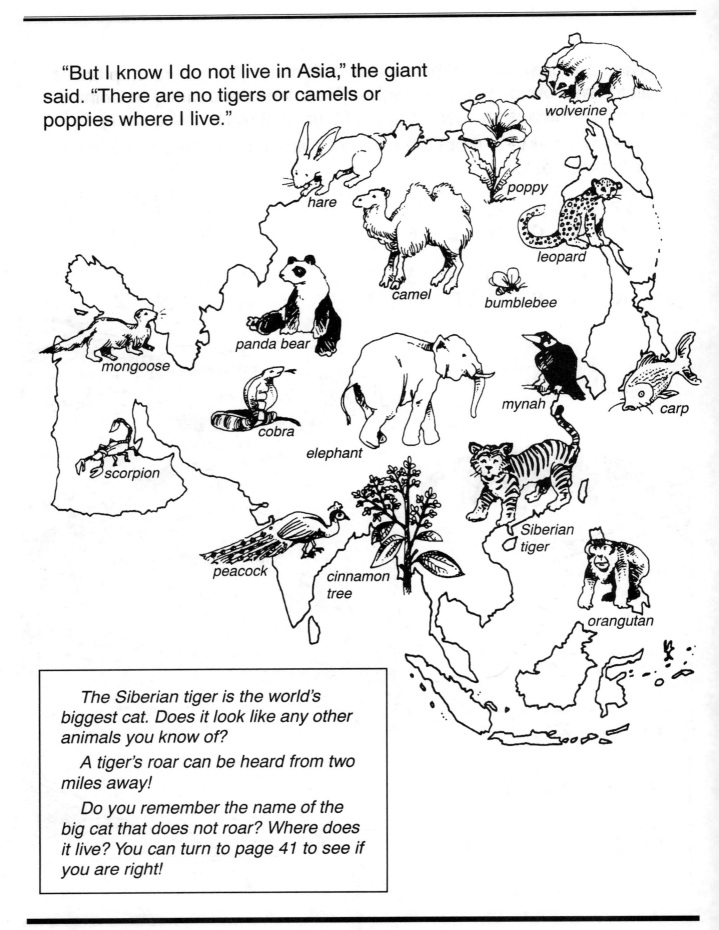

wolverine

poppy

hare

leopard

camel

bumblebee

panda bear

mongoose

mynah

carp

cobra

elephant

scorpion

Siberian tiger

peacock

cinnamon tree

orangutan

The Siberian tiger is the world's biggest cat. Does it look like any other animals you know of?

A tiger's roar can be heard from two miles away!

Do you remember the name of the big cat that does not roar? Where does it live? You can turn to page 41 to see if you are right!

Japan is an island country in Asia. You can see it on the map on page 52. Look for the city of Tokyo. The highest mountain in Japan is Mount Fuji. Many people climb it each year. Most climbers make the long hike during the summer, when the mountain is not covered with snow. There are stone huts along the way where climbers can rest.

Follow the maze from START to END. Help the climbers get to the top of Mount Fuji.

AFRICA

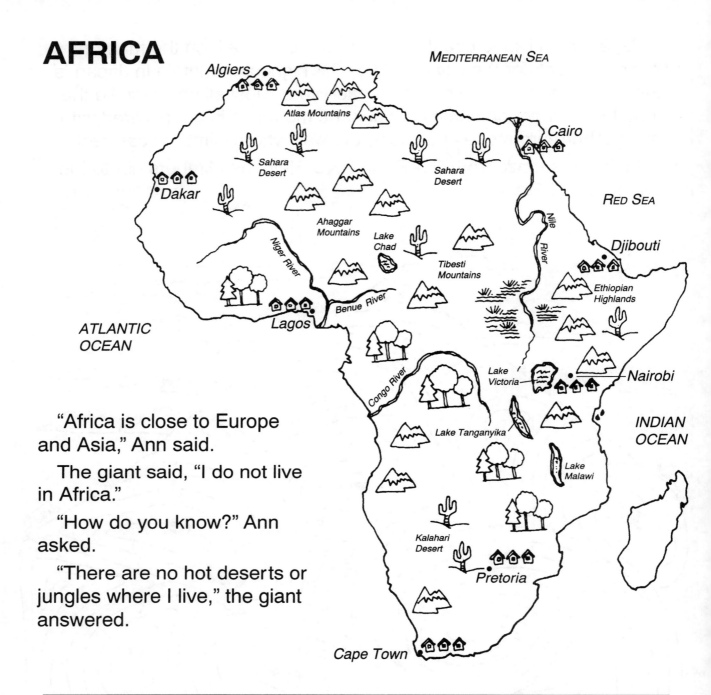

MEDITERRANEAN SEA

Algiers

Atlas Mountains

Cairo

RED SEA

Sahara Desert

Sahara Desert

Dakar

Djibouti

Ahaggar Mountains

Lake Chad

Nile River

Ethiopian Highlands

Niger River

Tibesti Mountains

Benue River

Lagos

ATLANTIC OCEAN

Congo River

Lake Victoria

Nairobi

INDIAN OCEAN

Lake Tanganyika

Lake Malawi

Kalahari Desert

Pretoria

Cape Town

"Africa is close to Europe and Asia," Ann said.

The giant said, "I do not live in Africa."

"How do you know?" Ann asked.

"There are no hot deserts or jungles where I live," the giant answered.

Africa is a big continent. Suppose you are in Cairo and you want to go to Cape Town. In which direction would you travel?

Would you cross over rivers? What else might you see on your way?

Some people who live in Africa make their houses out of grass. How would you make a grass house?

Would a grass house keep you warm or cool?

"Also, there are no date trees or crocodiles or elephants where I live," the giant said.

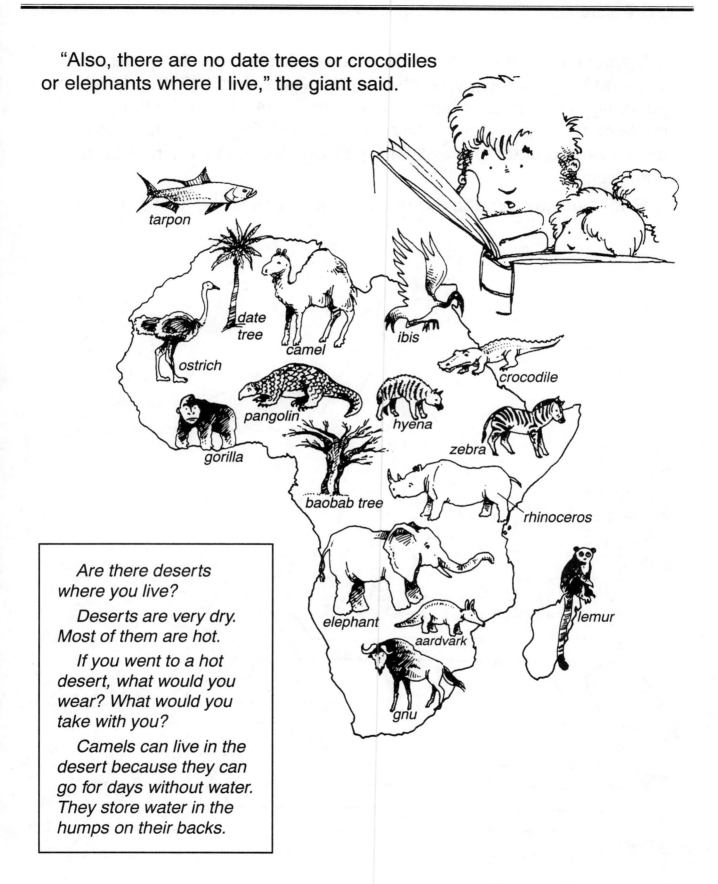

tarpon
date tree
camel
ostrich
ibis
crocodile
pangolin
hyena
zebra
gorilla
baobab tree
rhinoceros
elephant
aardvark
lemur
gnu

Are there deserts where you live?

Deserts are very dry. Most of them are hot.

If you went to a hot desert, what would you wear? What would you take with you?

Camels can live in the desert because they can go for days without water. They store water in the humps on their backs.

Egypt is a country in the north of Africa. It is famous for some very large buildings called pyramids. The pyramids were built thousands of years ago as tombs, or burial places, for Egypt's kings. Each pyramid contains many passages. Some are used to bring in air, and some are for workers to enter and exit. One passage leads to the king's burial chamber.

Find your way through the maze of passages to the king's chamber.

There are many interesting animals that live on the continent of Africa. Look at the pictures below. Write a sentence that answers the question about each animal.

Why does the giraffe have a long neck?

_____

_____

_____

How do the zebra's stripes help it to survive? _____

_____

_____

Why is it good that a hippo's eyes are located near the top of its head? _____

_____

_____

How do the leopard's spots help it catch its prey?

_____

_____

_____

AUSTRALIA

Ann turned to a map of Australia. "Maybe you live here," she said.
Ann read in the book that Australia is the smallest continent.

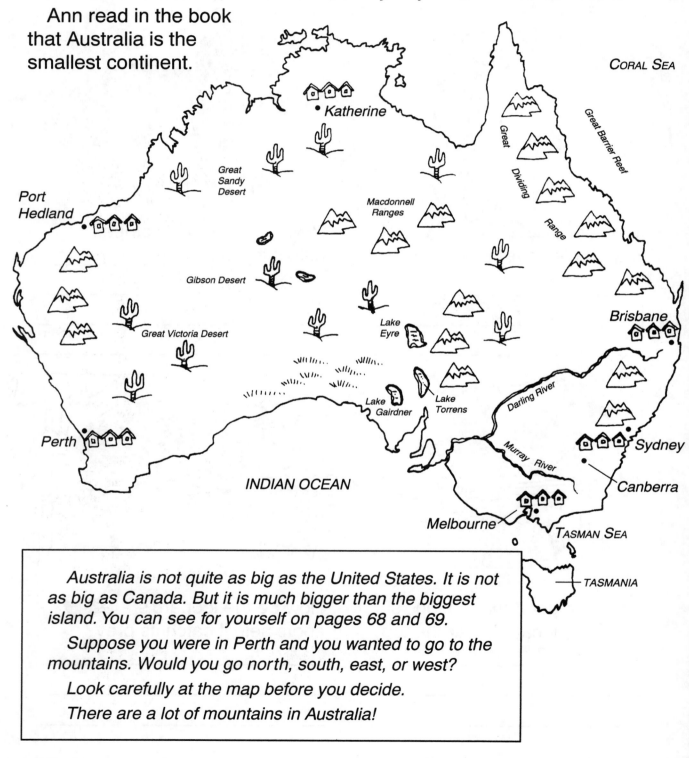

Australia is not quite as big as the United States. It is not as big as Canada. But it is much bigger than the biggest island. You can see for yourself on pages 68 and 69.

Suppose you were in Perth and you wanted to go to the mountains. Would you go north, south, east, or west?

Look carefully at the map before you decide.

There are a lot of mountains in Australia!

"There are kangaroos and emus and koalas in Australia," the giant said. "But there are none of those animals where I live."

"Have you ever seen a kangaroo?" Ann asked the giant. "Kangaroo mothers carry their babies in pouches that look like pockets. I think that sounds uncomfortable!" she said, laughing.

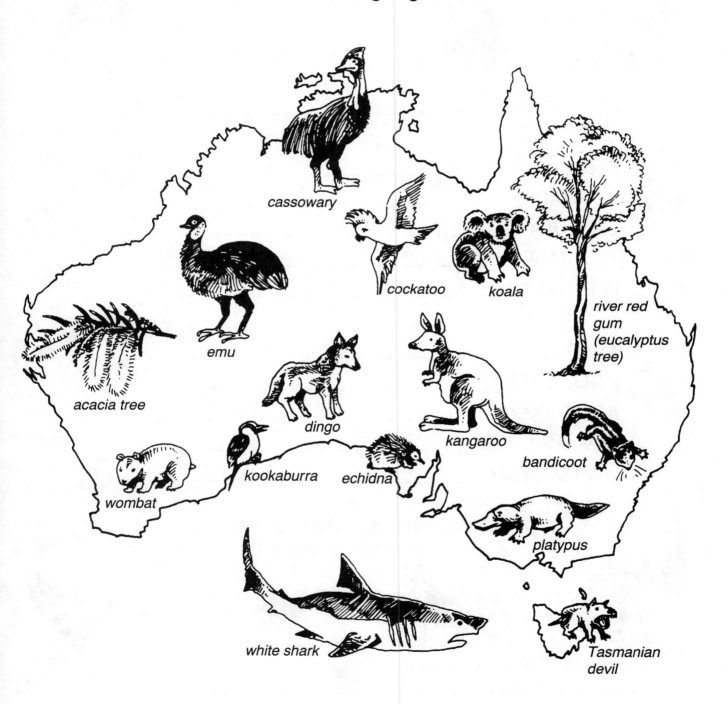

cassowary

cockatoo

koala

river red gum (eucalyptus tree)

emu

acacia tree

dingo

kangaroo

bandicoot

kookaburra

echidna

wombat

platypus

white shark

Tasmanian devil

Unscramble the names of these Australian animals. Then point to the picture that matches each name. Use page 61 as a reference if you need help.

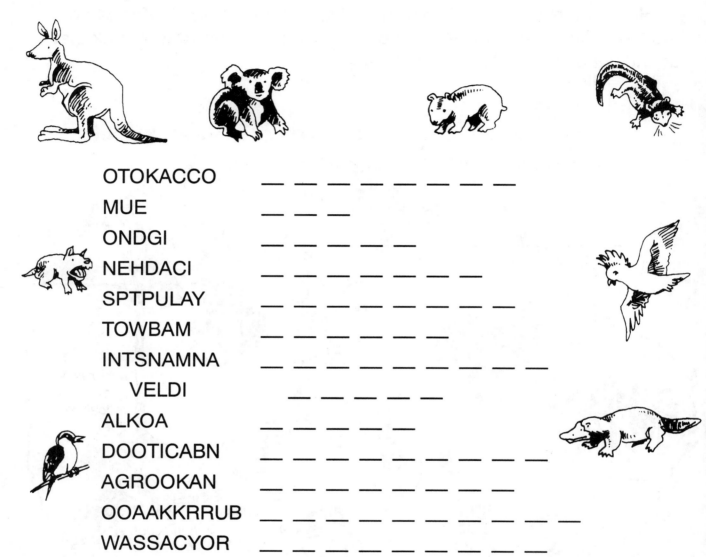

OTOKACCO   _ _ _ _ _ _ _ _

MUE   _ _ _

ONDGI   _ _ _ _ _

NEHDACI   _ _ _ _ _ _ _

SPTPULAY   _ _ _ _ _ _ _ _

TOWBAM   _ _ _ _ _ _

INTSNAMNA   _ _ _ _ _ _ _ _ _

VELDI   _ _ _ _ _

ALKOA   _ _ _ _ _

DOOTICABN   _ _ _ _ _ _ _ _ _

AGROOKAN   _ _ _ _ _ _ _ _

OOAAKKRRUB   _ _ _ _ _ _ _ _ _ _

WASSACYOR   _ _ _ _ _ _ _ _ _

Use an encyclopedia to find out more about these animals.

Kangaroos belong to a group of mammals called marsupials. Most marsupials give birth to very tiny babies. The babies live for some time in a pouch on their mothers' stomachs.

There are several kinds of kangaroos. They are all different sizes. Use the clues below to help you label the pictures of kangaroos.

- The **eastern gray kangaroo** is larger than the **wallaby**.
- The **quokkas kangaroo** is about the size of a rabbit.
- The **eastern gray kangaroo** is not as tall as the **red kangaroo**.
- The **wallaby** is smaller than the **red kangaroo**.

ISLANDS

Ann turned the page. "Look, here are some islands," she said. "Do you live on an island?"

"I do not live on Greenland," the giant said, "even though it has ice, like my home. Greenland is close to the North Pole."

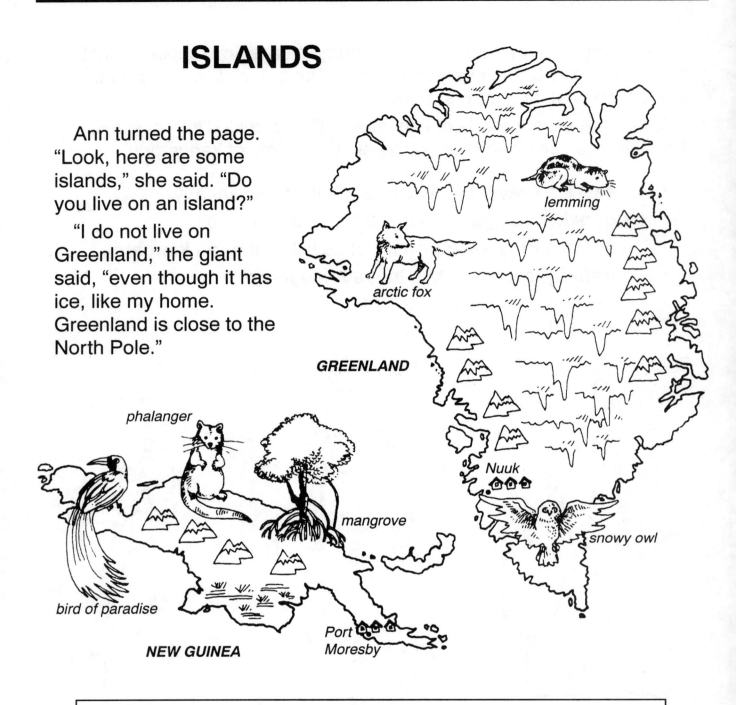

GREENLAND

NEW GUINEA

Some of these pictures of islands were drawn bigger so you can see them better. Greenland is much larger than New Guinea, New Zealand, or Madagascar.

Is Greenland the largest island in the world? You can turn to pages 68 and 69 to find out! There you will be able to see how the islands and the continents compare to each other in size.

"Here are some more islands," Ann said. "Do you live on Madagascar or New Zealand?"

"No, I do not live on an island," the giant said.

MADAGASCAR

hammerhead

traveler's tree

porcupine globefish

Androna Volcano

lemur

chameleon

Antananarivo

praying mantis

NEW ZEALAND

Wanganui River

Wellington

bat

cormorant

pine tree

Christchurch

kiwi

Have you ever been on land that has water all around it? That is an island. Because some islands are so big, we call them continents.

Australia has water all around it, but Australia is not an island. Because it is so big, Australia is a continent.

Imagine what it would be like to live with water all around you.

How would you get to your island? Would you walk? Would you swim? Would you go by boat or by airplane? Would you go by car?

Find the names of many of the world's islands hidden in the word search below. Remember that names may appear from left to right, right to left, or up and down.

GREENLAND   **NEW ZEALAND**   **BERMUDA**
ICELAND   **AZORES**   **CRETE**
MADAGASCAR   **CANARY**   **CUBA**
GALAPAGOS   **HAWAII**   **PUERTO RICO**

```
P D N A L A E Z W E N P
U D N A L Y A L P L U M
E P U A Z O R E S D D I
R I C L I C E L A N D S
T I A E N U G F P E L O
O A N U A B C E K A M G
R W A I L A R T S U A A
I A R A C R U E T L D P
C H E N P L Z R E T U A
O T R L V O M C T G M L
I M A D A G A S C A R A
B N Y R A N A C A I E G
D N A L N E E R G D B T
```

Look for all of these islands on a globe of the world.
Can you find any others?

The country called Ireland is on an island. The land is so full of green fields and hills that it is often called The Emerald Isle. Long ago, many castle homes were built in Ireland. They protected families from their enemies. One of these is called Bunratty Castle.

Complete the missing half of Bunratty Castle. (**Hint:** The castle is symmetrical. This means that it is exactly the same on both sides.) When you are finished, color the grass and trees around the castle in beautiful emerald green. Color the water blue.

THE WORLD

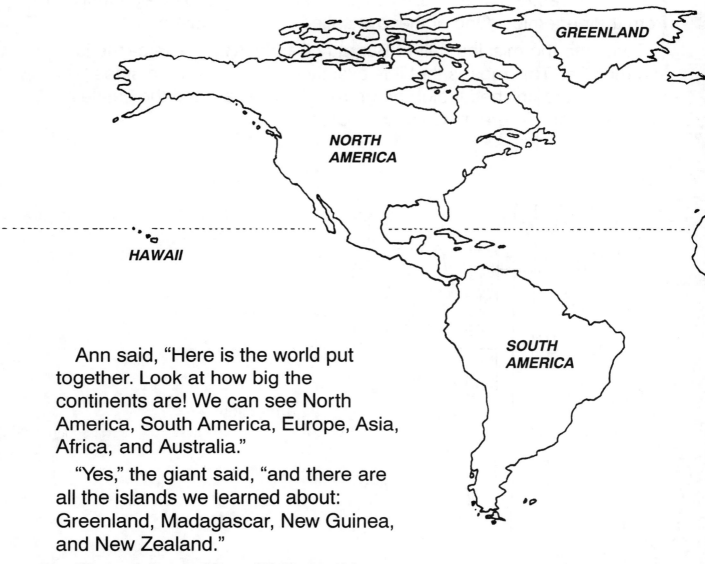

Ann said, "Here is the world put together. Look at how big the continents are! We can see North America, South America, Europe, Asia, Africa, and Australia."

"Yes," the giant said, "and there are all the islands we learned about: Greenland, Madagascar, New Guinea, and New Zealand."

"Do not forget Hawaii!" Ann said.

Did you remember that Hawaii is not just a group of islands?
It is something else, too. What is it?
What country is Hawaii a part of?

The giant shook his head sadly. "We have looked at all these places, and I do not live anywhere here," he said.

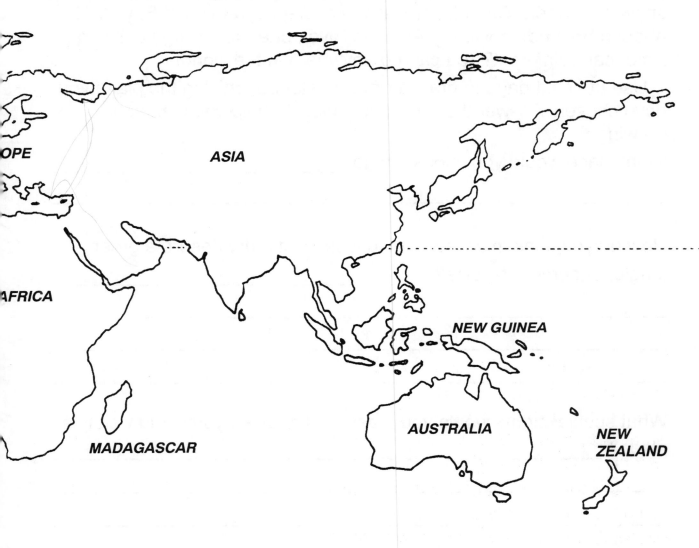

Do you know where the giant lives?

His home is not on an island. It does not have polar bears, coyotes, maple trees, or redwood trees. It does not have jaguars, hedgehogs, tigers, elephants, or kangaroos.

The giant's home is not a hot desert, but it does have something very cold. Do you remember what that is?

Where can the giant's home be?

Now that you have seen quite a bit of the world, what place would you most like to visit? Would you like to ride a dogsled through the snow of northern Canada, or visit the ancient pyramids of Egypt? How about a boat ride down the Amazon River, or a trip through a South American rainforest? You can go anywhere in the world!

Use the next page to draw a travel poster advertising the place you have chosen. Answer the questions below to help you plan your drawing.

What place would you choose to go? _____

_____

How do you think this place would look? Is it a dry desert, a green jungle, or something else? _____

_____

_____

_____

What special sights would you most want to see if you could visit this place? _____

_____

_____

What kinds of things would you be able to do in this place?

_____

_____

_____

_____

_____

_____

THE OCEAN

"Look!" Ann said. "There are lots of animals that live in the ocean. Maybe you live in the ocean!"

"No, I do not live there," the giant said. "I cannot swim."

seal

porpoise

salmon

lobster

eel

sea horse

piranha

ray

killer whale

marlin

Would you like to live in the ocean? What kind of home would you have?

Look at the map of the world. Do you see more water or land on the Earth?

It is hard to tell, but there is lots more water than land.

Look for the group of fish swimming together below. This group has a funny name. It is called a school of fish. Can you think of a reason why?

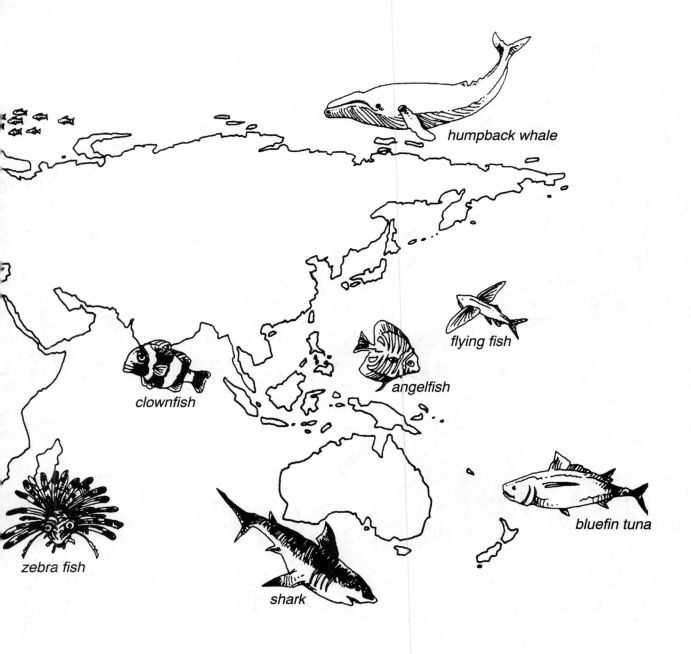

humpback whale

flying fish

angelfish

clownfish

bluefin tuna

zebra fish

shark

Search the ocean for as many different kinds of sea creatures as you can find. Match each creature to a name below.

octopus	**sea star**	**jelly fish**	**shark**
whale	**dolphin**	**angelfish**	**zebra fish**
clown fish	**flying fish**	**flounder**	**eel**
ray	**sea lion**	**seahorse**	**clam**

Find some of the world's oceans and seas in the word search below. Remember that words can be found from left to right, right to left, or even up and down.

PACIFIC   **CASPIAN**   **ARABIAN**
ATLANTIC   **MEDITERRANEAN**   **CARIBBEAN**
ARCTIC   **RED**   **CORAL**
INDIAN   **DEAD**   **BLACK**

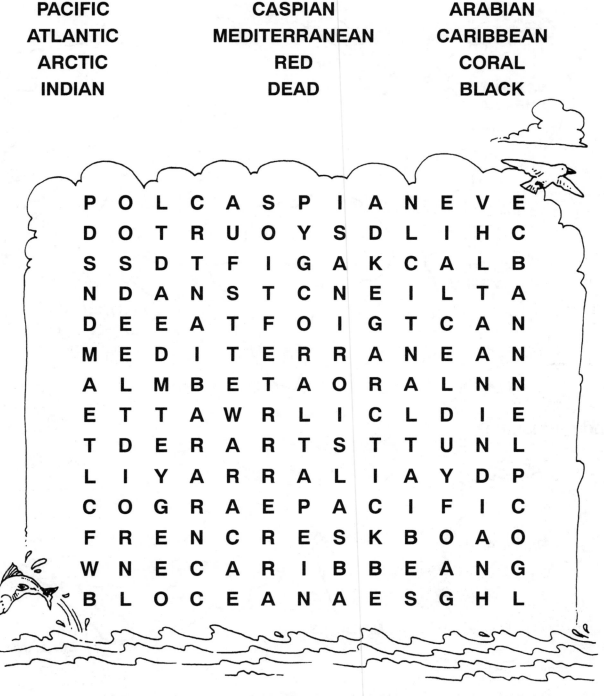

```
P O L C A S P I A N E V E
D O T R U O Y S D L I H C
S S D T F I G A K C A L B
N D A N S T C N E I L T A
D E E A T F O I G T C A N
M E D I T E R R A N E A N
A L M B E T A O R A L N N
E T T A W R L I C L D I E
T D E R A R T S T T U N L
L I Y A R R A L I A Y D P
C O G R A E P A C I F I C
F R E N C R E S K B O A O
W N E C A R I B B E A N G
B L O C E A N A E S G H L
```

Look for each ocean and sea on a globe of the world!

WHERE DOES THE GIANT LIVE?

Ann said, "No wonder you are lost! We have looked at six continents . . .

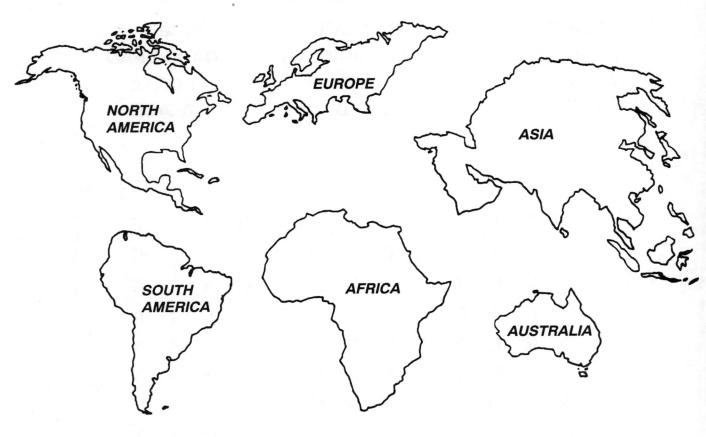

and four islands . . .

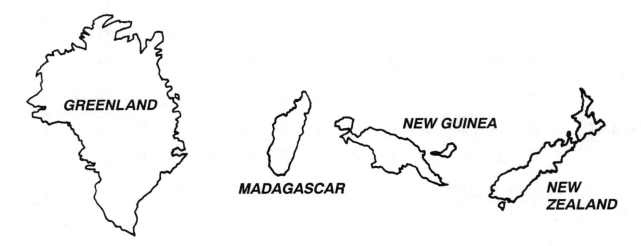

and in the ocean. You do not live in any of those places. Where on
Earth do you live?"

THE GIANT'S HOME

The giant and Ann looked at the book.

"There is the South Pole," Ann said, "down at the bottom of the Earth. It is in Antarctica, the seventh continent."

"Look!" the giant said. "There is a penguin. There are penguins where I live! I must live in Antarctica!"

"What a funny-looking bird!" Ann said.

"Penguins cannot fly," the giant said. "They are good swimmers and stay close to home."

Then the giant jumped for joy. "Hurray!" he said. "If I just walk south, I will get home, too! Good-bye."

"Good-bye," Ann said. "I will miss you."

"I will write to you," the giant called. "I know your address."

If the giant walks south from where Ann lives, what continents will he go through? You can check your answer on page 68.

Most people think all penguins look exactly alike, but that is not true. There are many different kinds of penguins. Emperor penguins are four feet tall. Some other penguins may grow to only 12 inches in height! All penguins have chubby bodies and flippers instead of wings. Their black-and-white coats are covered with waterproof feathers.

Look carefully at the penguins. Some of them have a matching partner. Can you find the pairs of penguins that are exactly alike?

Use the code to find out the message being sent by the spaceship.
Fill in the message at the bottom of the page.

A B C D E F G H I J K L M N O P Q R S T U V W X Y Z

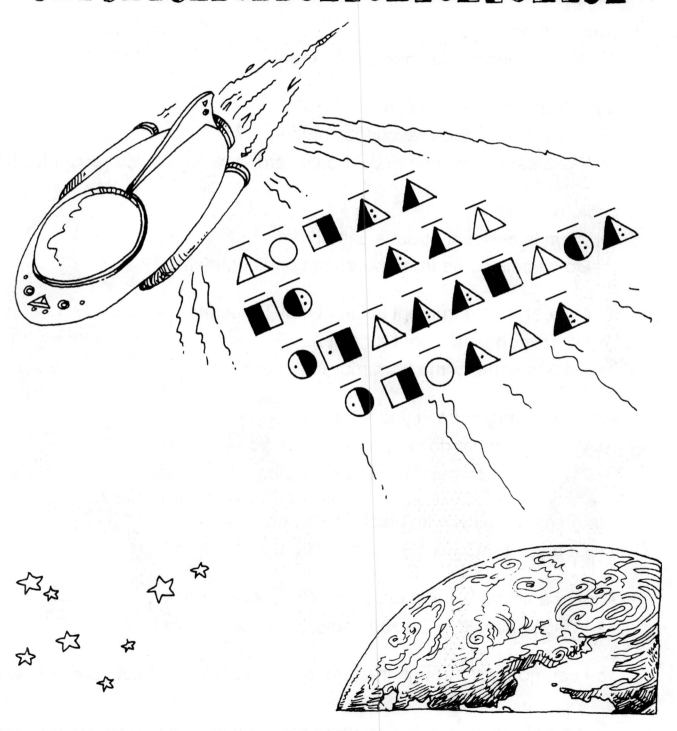

79

A FIELD TRIP

See if you can take a trip to the zoo. When you get there, look at all the different animals.

Look at the tigers.
  • What continent do tigers come from?

Does the zoo have a raccoon?
  • What continent do raccoons come from?
  • If you saw a raccoon in your backyard, how would you recognize it?

Look for a camel.
  • What is different about a camel?
  • Do camels come from more than one continent?

If you hear a loud trumpet noise, it may be an elephant.
  • What is unusual about an elephant?
  • Do elephants come from more than one continent?

Are there kangaroos in your zoo?
  • What continent do kangaroos come from?
  • Do you remember what is special about kangaroos?

Penguins are birds with black-and-white suits.
  • Can you remember what is different about these birds?

A lot of animals in the zoo come from faraway places.
  • Which animals in the zoo come from North America?

You can go back through the pages of this book to check your answers!